Ask Hannah!

Written by Cynthia Stierle
Based on the series created by Michael Poryes and Rich Correll & Barry O'Brien

A girl can dream.

Reader's Digest
Children's Books®

Pleasantville, New York • Montréal, Québec • Bath, United Kingdom

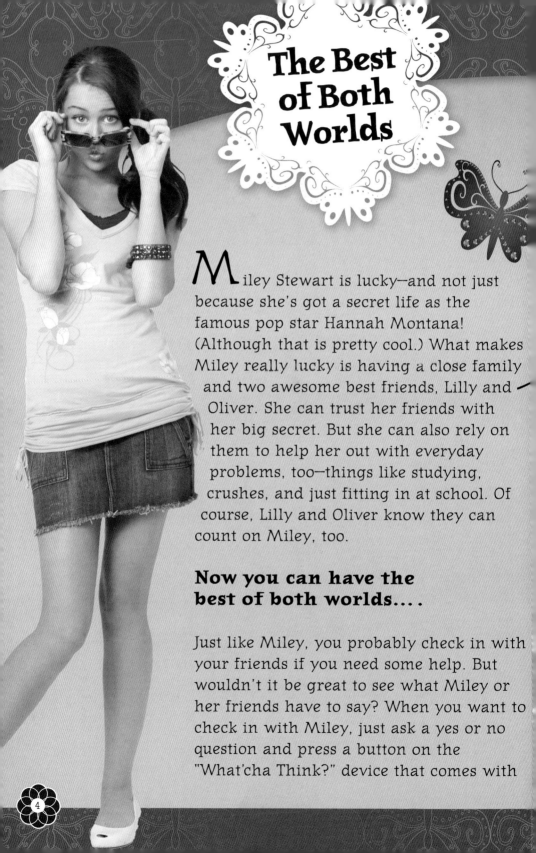

The Best of Both Worlds

Miley Stewart is lucky—and not just because she's got a secret life as the famous pop star Hannah Montana! (Although that is pretty cool.) What makes Miley really lucky is having a close family and two awesome best friends, Lilly and Oliver. She can trust her friends with her big secret. But she can also rely on them to help her out with everyday problems, too—things like studying, crushes, and just fitting in at school. Of course, Lilly and Oliver know they can count on Miley, too.

Now you can have the best of both worlds....

Just like Miley, you probably check in with your friends if you need some help. But wouldn't it be great to see what Miley or her friends have to say? When you want to check in with Miley, just ask a yes or no question and press a button on the "What'cha Think?" device that comes with

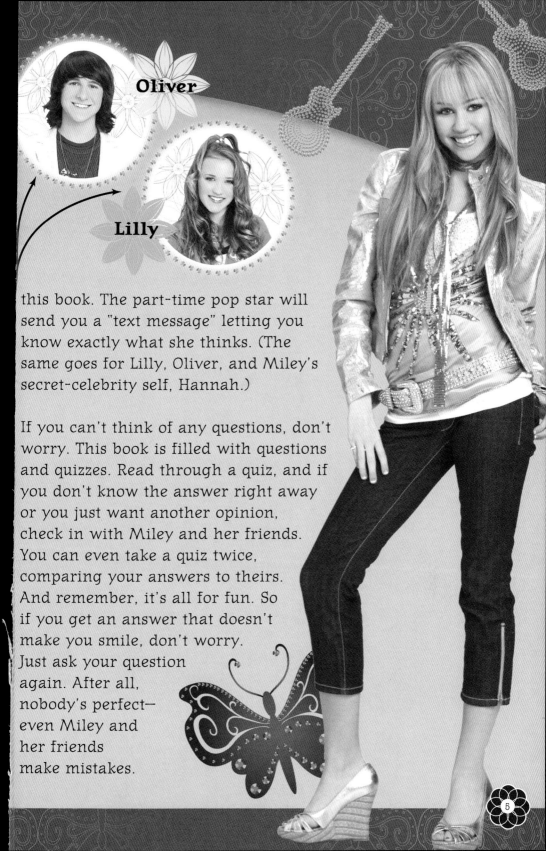

Oliver

Lilly

this book. The part-time pop star will send you a "text message" letting you know exactly what she thinks. (The same goes for Lilly, Oliver, and Miley's secret-celebrity self, Hannah.)

If you can't think of any questions, don't worry. This book is filled with questions and quizzes. Read through a quiz, and if you don't know the answer right away or you just want another opinion, check in with Miley and her friends. You can even take a quiz twice, comparing your answers to theirs. And remember, it's all for fun. So if you get an answer that doesn't make you smile, don't worry. Just ask your question again. After all, nobody's perfect— even Miley and her friends make mistakes.

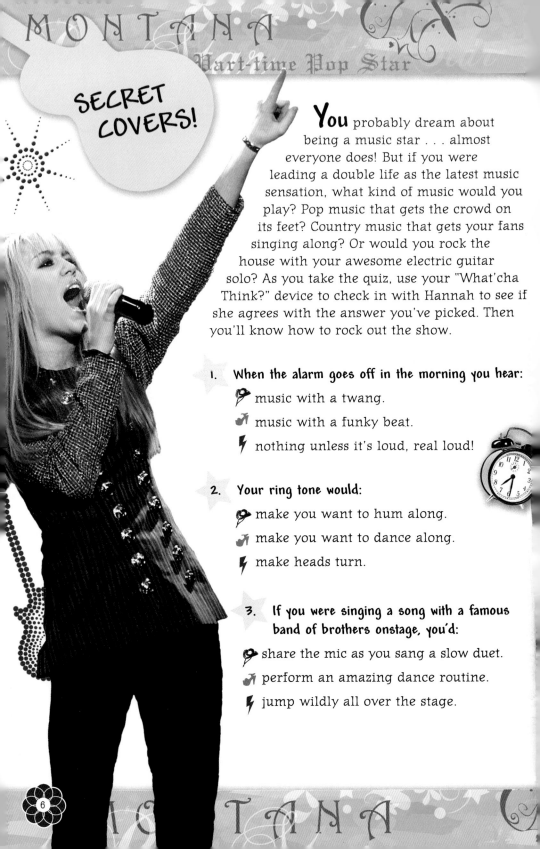

SECRET COVERS!

You probably dream about being a music star . . . almost everyone does! But if you were leading a double life as the latest music sensation, what kind of music would you play? Pop music that gets the crowd on its feet? Country music that gets your fans singing along? Or would you rock the house with your awesome electric guitar solo? As you take the quiz, use your "What'cha Think?" device to check in with Hannah to see if she agrees with the answer you've picked. Then you'll know how to rock out the show.

1. **When the alarm goes off in the morning you hear:**
   - music with a twang.
   - music with a funky beat.
   - nothing unless it's loud, real loud!

2. **Your ring tone would:**
   - make you want to hum along.
   - make you want to dance along.
   - make heads turn.

3. **If you were singing a song with a famous band of brothers onstage, you'd:**
   - share the mic as you sang a slow duet.
   - perform an amazing dance routine.
   - jump wildly all over the stage.

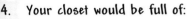
4. **Your closet would be full of:**

- 🌸 pretty skirts and cute boots.
- ⚜ skinny jeans and lots of bling.
- ⚡ graphic T's and lots of black.

5. **Your stage name could be:**

- 🌸 SueAnn Pecan.
- ⚜ Ashley McFashley.
- ⚡ Lereign Maine.

6. **Your latest CD might be called:**

- 🌸 *Hearts and Home.*
- ⚜ *Hands in the Air.*
- ⚡ *Rock On.*

7. **You'd launch your new CD:**

- 🌸 at a big ole party in Nashville.
- ⚜ at the hottest club in LA.
- ⚡ at an underground club in NYC.

8. **Your tour bus would be filled with:**

- 🌸 all the comforts of home.
- ⚜ all the latest tech gadgets.
- ⚡ lots of guitars and amps.

WHO ARE YOU?

"MOSTLY 🌸'S:" You're a country girl at heart. You're sure to warm the hearts of all your fans with your down-home music.

"MOSTLY ⚜'S:" You're a pop princess. The crowd is on its feet and moving to the beat of your latest hit song.

"MOSTLY ⚡'S:" You love rock 'n' roll! Fans everywhere play air guitar when they hear your awesome sound.

TRUE FRIENDS

Miley, Lilly, and Oliver are best buds, and they like to hang out together. Spending time with a bunch of friends is fun, because everyone brings something different to the party. No, not chips and salsa! You and your friends all have special personality traits that make group get-togethers a blast. What do you add to your mix of friends? Answer yes, maybe, or no to find out. Then ask Lilly and Oliver what they think—and see if you agree.

1. Your friend impulsively buys a wild new outfit that was in a store display. But when she tries it on, it's really . . . out there. Do you gently tell her to return it?

YES — people will probably laugh if she wears it to school.
MAYBE — but first you'll see if some changes can make it wearable.
NO — you buy one so you can both wear it on the same day.
    Maybe you'll start a fashion trend!

2. You've just been invited to a big party—but your best bud hasn't been asked. Do you check to see if you can bring her along?

YES — it won't be the same without her.
MAYBE — first you'll see if she wants to go.
NO — you'll just bring her anyway.

3. Your BFF just broke up with her boyfriend and you've been talking to her for an hour. She wants to keep talking, but your favorite TV show is coming on. Do you keep talking?

YES — you can catch the show some other time.
MAYBE — you offer to text her while you watch.
NO — but you encourage her to watch the show, too, to take her mind off of things.

4. OMG! Your friend walked into the cafeteria with toilet paper stuck to her shoe. She leaves right away, but texts you to make sure no one else noticed. You saw people laughing, but you're not sure what they were laughing about.
You text back...

YES — NO1 noticed.
MAYBE — IDK
NO — a few. NBD

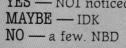

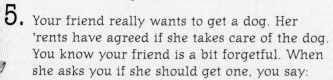

5. Your friend really wants to get a dog. Her 'rents have agreed if she takes care of the dog. You know your friend is a bit forgetful. When she asks you if she should get one, you say:

YES — you'll text her to remind her to feed and walk it.

MAYBE — you get some dog care books to make sure she understands the responsibility.

NO — but you offer to go with her to the dog pound to walk the dogs there. Then she'll know if she's ready for her own.

6. Your friend is trying out for the cheering squad and wants you to try out, too. Backflips aren't your thing. You say:

YES — you would've had to learn how to do a backflip at some point anyway.

MAYBE — at the very least you'll cheer her on.

NO — but you'll try out for the soccer team at the same time.

7. You and your friends are deciding what movie to see. Would you pick a touching dramatic flick?

YES — those stories are always sweet.

MAYBE — if it got good reviews.

NO — you'd rather have a LOL comedy.

8. You've won concert tickets from a radio station. Two of your friends love the band, but you can only bring one. Do you flip a coin?

YES — so they'll know you don't play favorites.

MAYBE — or you'll see if they can make the decision.

NO — you'll run a silly contest for them and take the winner.

SCORING: 1 point for every YES, 2 points for every MAYBE, and 3 points for every NO.

8–13: Kind and caring. You're always aware of your friends' feelings, and you'll be there for them even if it means putting yourself out.

14–19: Loyal and level. You're a good friend, and you try to play fair all the time.

20–24: Fun and fearless. You go your own way—but your friends know it's fun to be along for the ride.

MAKE ME UP BEFORE YOU GO-GO

Miley gives herself a makeover all the time, going from an ordinary teen to pop sensation Hannah Montana. She's even given Lilly a makeover for a school dance, turning Lilly from SK8TR girl to D8TR girl. Of course, Lilly didn't really need a makeover . . . and you probably don't need one, either. But makeovers are fun, so answer yes or no to find out whether you should get one. Then get a guy's opinion; check in with Oliver to see what he thinks—and if he doesn't give you a definite answer, try again.

1. I'm often at the mall or shopping online.
>**YES** — I love to look at the latest styles.
>**NO** — my mom does my shopping.

2. My friends always want to copy my clothes.
>**YES** — they all like my stuff.
>**NO** — I have a look all my own.

3. I change my hairstyle all the time.
>**YES** — barrettes, hair bands, up or down, it's all fun.
>**NO** — it's been the same since forever.

4. You can never have too many shoes.
>**YES** — 'nuff said.
>**NO** — a pair of sneakers is all I need.

5. I really don't need much makeup.
>**YES** — I let me show through.
>**NO** — I'm under the eyeliner somewhere.

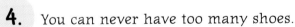

6. It doesn't take me long to do my hair in the morning.
>**YES** — my style is pretty simple.
>**NO** — I need an extra hour just for the blow-dryer.

7. I keep a nail file in my locker.
   YES — I'm ready for a nail emergency.
   NO — I usually bite them, anyway.

8. A locker mirror? A must-have.
   YES — a quick check makes me feel better.
   NO — it doesn't much matter.

9. I need to decide the night before what to wear to school.
   YES — it would take way too much time in the morning.
   NO — I could get dressed in the dark
      (matching is optional).

10. When I see a new style, I'll try it on even if I don't think it will work on me.
   YES — sometimes you get a nice surprise!
   NO — why bother?

SCORING: Give yourself 1 point for every YES answer.

0-3: A MINI MAKEOVER. You're comfortable with your look, but you might be overdue for a change. You don't have to change who you are, or wear things that aren't your style. But flip through a fashion magazine to see if there are some new styles that appeal to you.

4-6: MAKEOVER . . . MAYBE. You're not afraid to change some things, but you probably could use a little boost. Maybe it's time to clean out your closet to make room for a few new pieces.

7-10: MAKEOVER MAVEN. You are probably the one giving fashion advice to your friends. It's great, but if you find a style you love, don't be afraid to stick with it for a little while.

Psst! Even if you don't need to change your look, it's always fun to get together with your friends and give yourself makeovers—especially if you're having a slumber party. Buy some inexpensive hair accessories and makeup items so each guest has her own. (You already know not to share makeup and hairbrushes.) Then have fun styling the night away!

WILD WARDROBE

ADMIT IT: you'd LOVE to have a closet like Hannah Montana's! After all, she has designer clothes, juicy jewelry, and cute shoes. But if you could have any of her wardrobe–clothes, jewelry, or shoes–which would you most want to see in your closet? Follow the path to find out. Then check with Hannah Montana to see if she wants to steer you in another direction. (It is her closet, after all!)

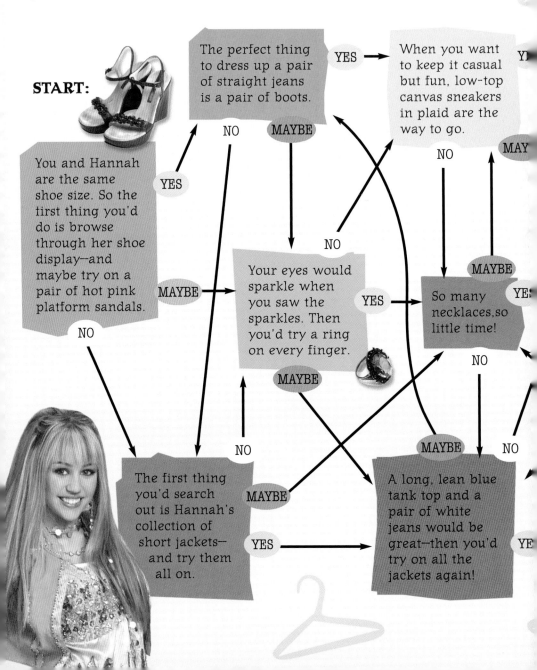

START:

You and Hannah are the same shoe size. So the first thing you'd do is browse through her shoe display—and maybe try on a pair of hot pink platform sandals.

The perfect thing to dress up a pair of straight jeans is a pair of boots.

When you want to keep it casual but fun, low-top canvas sneakers in plaid are the way to go.

Your eyes would sparkle when you saw the sparkles. Then you'd try a ring on every finger.

So many necklaces, so little time!

The first thing you'd search out is Hannah's collection of short jackets—and try them all on.

A long, lean blue tank top and a pair of white jeans would be great—then you'd try on all the jackets again!

YES • NO • MAYBE

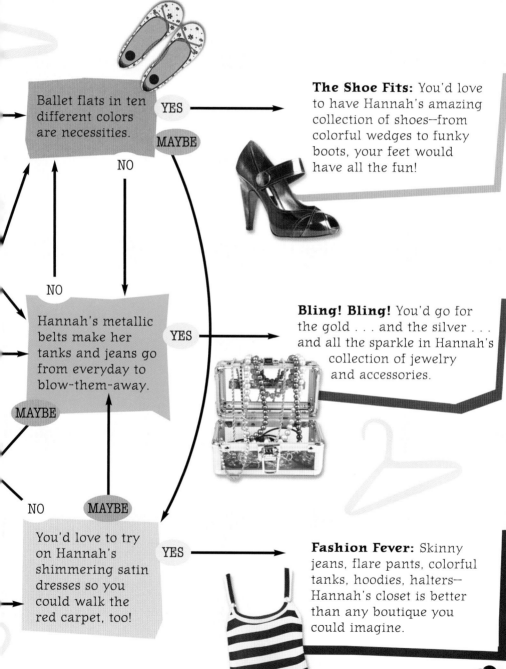

Ballet flats in ten different colors are necessities.

YES

MAYBE

NO

The Shoe Fits: You'd love to have Hannah's amazing collection of shoes—from colorful wedges to funky boots, your feet would have all the fun!

NO

Hannah's metallic belts make her tanks and jeans go from everyday to blow-them-away.

YES

Bling! Bling! You'd go for the gold . . . and the silver . . . and all the sparkle in Hannah's collection of jewelry and accessories.

MAYBE

NO   MAYBE

You'd love to try on Hannah's shimmering satin dresses so you could walk the red carpet, too!

YES

Fashion Fever: Skinny jeans, flare pants, colorful tanks, hoodies, halters—Hannah's closet is better than any boutique you could imagine.

— SCHOOL ZONE —

At school Miley is just an average girl—and that's exactly what she wants to be. And like all average girls, Miley runs into everyday problems at school. You know, like the time she and Lilly found themselves at the bottom of the popularity list, right after Dandruff Danny! Since Miley knows what school is really like, you can use your "What'cha Think?" device to ask her a few questions about school, like the ones below. Then Miley will send you a "text message" so you can see what she thinks. And don't forget to check in with Lilly and Oliver, too.

1. My band concert is coming up. Will I remember what I practiced?

2. If schedules change, will I still have lunch period with some of my friends?

3. Will my locker stay organized?

4. Will I get a lot of homework?

5. Will I make lots of new friends this year?

6. Club activities are fun. Should I try a new club?

7. Is there something I'd like to eat in the cafeteria?

8. Will I be able to handle any fashion emergencies?

9. If I have to do an oral report, will I sound okay?

10. Will I ever get sent to the principal's office?

11. The school dance is coming up. Will it be a blast?

12. Should I try out for the cheerleading squad?

* Miley's Tip—

If you get an answer that makes your stomach butterflies do backflips, it's *SO* not the end of the world. The answers, like life, are what you make of them. So just ask the question again or try to put a positive spin on the answer. After all, even if you don't remember everything you've practiced for the school concert, it might mean you'll miss only one note. *NBD!* Or if you have to do an oral report, maybe you won't sound *OKAY*, you'll sound **FANTASTIC!**

EXERCISE, ANYONE?

Miley might not always be the best athlete in school. But maybe she's just not playing the right games. After all, exercise is great. Do you know what game is perfect for you? After you've taken the quiz for yourself, check with Oliver to find out if he agrees. Then see if you can help Miley and Lilly find their games, too.

1. You're old enough to go to the gym with your mom.
She wants to know what you'd like to do. You suggest:
- **A.** ditching the gym for the local skate park.
- **B.** taking a spinning class.
- **C.** running on a treadmill while she takes a yoga class.

2. When you play on a team, everyone knows that you're:
- **A.** in it for the fun.
- **B.** in it to win it.
- **C.** doing your best.

3. Exercising at the beach means:
- **A.** bodysurfing.
- **B.** a game of beach volleyball.
- **C.** going for a jog.

4. If you could win an Olympic medal,
you'd want it to be in:
- **A.** freestyle skiing.
- **B.** soccer or ice hockey.
- **C.** individual swimming or ice-skating.

5. If you won tickets to a sporting
event, you'd like to see:
- **A.** the X-Games.
- **B.** the World Cup.
- **C.** Wimbledon.

6. You watch sports on TV:
- **A.** when a surfing competition is on.
- **B.** whenever your fave team is playing.
- **C.** whenever your fave athlete is competing.

7. In gym class you love it when:
   A. you get to use the climbing wall.
   B. you play team games.
   C. you can choose your own game.

8. It feels great when:
   A. you create a new dance move.
   B. you help your team win.
   C. you beat your best performance.

9. The summer camp you'd like to attend is:
   A. an adventure camp that lets you blaze a new trail.
   B. a sports camp with other players from your team.
   C. a sailing camp that lets you sail solo.

10. If you won a gift card to a sporting-goods store, you'd buy:
   A. a skateboard.
   B. a soccer ball.
   C. a tennis racket.

Mostly A's: X-tremely Fun. You don't move unless you're having fun—and that means everything from sports like surfing and snowboarding to dancing the night away.

Mostly B's: Go Team. You play well with others and it shows—soccer, basketball, cheerleading, or lacrosse—it's all a team effort!

Mostly C's: Flying Solo. You go solo in the spotlight, so individual sports like swimming, gymnastics, or track and field are ones that might let you shine.

ARE WE FAMILY?

Miley loves her dad, Robby Ray, and she thinks her brother, Jackson, is pretty great, too. (But that doesn't mean she wants to share a bathroom with him!) Of course, they both help Miley keep her identity as Hannah Montana a secret. That could make everybody crazy, but Robby Ray is pretty relaxed and keeps everything and everyone calm. What's your family like? Are they laid-back and casual? Are they always on the go? Check out this quiz and find out—then try the quiz with Miley, Lilly, and Oliver to see what they say about their families.

1 The whole family sits down for dinner every night.
    A. YES — it's a great way to unwind.
    B. MAYBE — more like a few times a week.
    C. NO — unless sitting in the car counts.

2 On vacation we like to relax—at the beach, in the mountains, wherever.
    A. YES — that's our pace.
    B. MAYBE — but we'd also go sailing or hiking, too.
    C. NO — you'd find us at a theme park instead.

3 In the morning our house resembles an herbal tea commercial.
    A. YES — things are peaceful and quiet.
    B. MAYBE — if it's a weekend.
    C. NO — unless the commercial was shot in
            Grand Central Station.

4 We're always up for doing things on the spur of the moment.
    A. YES — surprises are fun.
    B. MAYBE — we'd have to check
        the schedule.
    C. NO — the schedule is so full
        we don't even have
        to check.

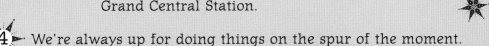
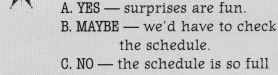
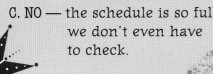

31
DECEMBER

5. My friends come to my house to chil-lax.
   A. YES — our house is a great hangout.
   B. MAYBE — I have to check with my 'rents first.
   C. NO — I'm usually at other people's houses.

6. A family Friday night would mean eating popcorn and playing board games.

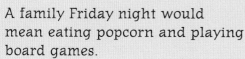

   A. YES — it's a great recipe for fun.
   B. MAYBE — or we might go out for pizza.
   C. NO — we'd probably get tickets to see something instead.

7. Your family rents some DVDs. They're most likely to be for-the-whole-family comedies.
   A. YES — then everyone can enjoy them.
   B. MAYBE — sometimes we get a mix.
   C. NO — we each pick our own flicks.

8. The inside of the family car is neat and organized.
   A. YES — we're all responsible for getting our things in and out.
   B. MAYBE — it can get a bit messy with everyone's stuff.
   C. NO — we actually call our car the rolling dining room.

MOSTLY A'S: Laid-back and Casual.
Your family is pretty relaxed about everything. While you may all be doing different things, you definitely set aside some time for everyone to be together and relax. But don't forget that playing together can be as much fun as relaxing together.

MOSTLY B'S: Middle of the Road.
You've all got places to go, but that doesn't mean you don't want to take a time-out once in a while to hang with the people you love.

MOSTLY C'S: Always on the Go.
Your family is involved in lots of different things, so you're all pulled in different directions. All the activity is great, but don't forget to take some time to just chill together.

COUNTRY ROADS . . .WHERE'S MY HOME?

Miley and her family moved from Tennessee to Malibu, California. They went from a view of the mountains to a view of the Pacific Ocean. Have you ever wondered if the view out of your front window would change? Where would you like live: in the country, in the city, or at the beach? Follow the path as you answer each question, or check with Lilly or Oliver to see if they know where you should relocate to someday.

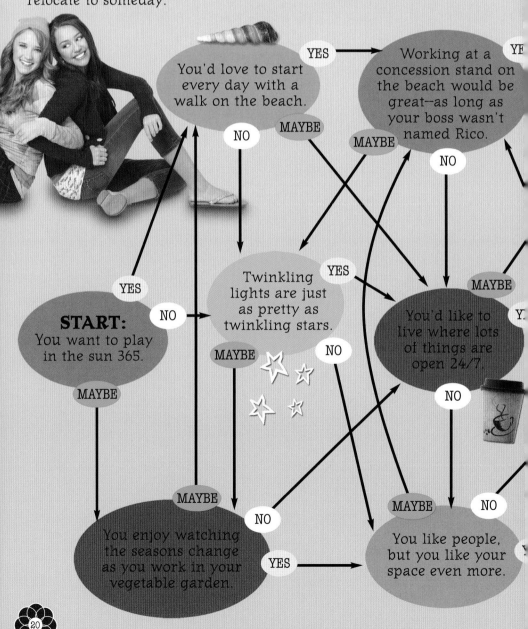

You'd love to start every day with a walk on the beach.

YES

Working at a concession stand on the beach would be great—as long as your boss wasn't named Rico.

YE

NO

MAYBE

MAYBE

NO

Twinkling lights are just as pretty as twinkling stars.

YES

MAYBE

YES

NO

START:
You want to play in the sun 365.

NO

MAYBE

NO

You'd like to live where lots of things are open 24/7.

Y.

MAYBE

NO

MAYBE

MAYBE

NO

You enjoy watching the seasons change as you work in your vegetable garden.

YES

You like people, but you like your space even more.

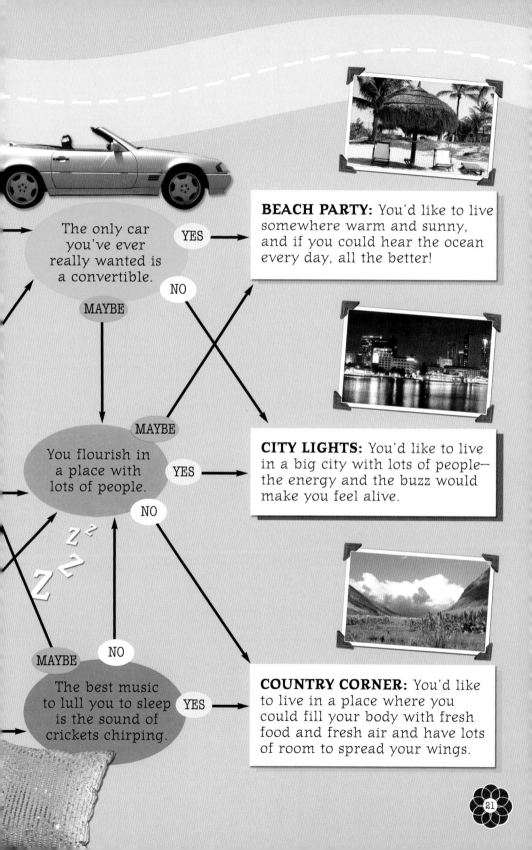

The only car you've ever really wanted is a convertible.

YES →

BEACH PARTY: You'd like to live somewhere warm and sunny, and if you could hear the ocean every day, all the better!

MAYBE

NO

MAYBE

You flourish in a place with lots of people.

YES →

CITY LIGHTS: You'd like to live in a big city with lots of people—the energy and the buzz would make you feel alive.

NO

MAYBE

NO

The best music to lull you to sleep is the sound of crickets chirping.

YES →

COUNTRY CORNER: You'd like to live in a place where you could fill your body with fresh food and fresh air and have lots of room to spread your wings.

Who Said?

THE QUESTIONS NEVER END ... but this book has to. So here are a few last questions for Miley and her friends. What do they see in your future? Ask the "What'cha Think?" device to find out. But don't forget the message of Hannah's music: You always have a choice, and you lead your own parade. So no matter what anyone says, do it your way! BBFN!

Will I win any awards?
Will I ever be on TV?
Will I ever get concert tickets?
Do I rock—at least sometimes

Is my BFF hiding something?
Should I try a new sport?
Will I get faster at texting?
Should I cut my hair?

Should I change my ring tone?
Will my game improve?
Should I join a new club?
Should I work on my dance moves?

Does my crush have a crush on me?
Should I plan a girls' night out?
Will I remember to turn in my homework?
Do I need a manicure?